THE SQUASHED TOMATO BOOK

ROGER SAWYER

Illustrations by Gary Davidson

B☘XTREE

First published in the UK 1993
by BOXTREE LIMITED, Broadwall House,
21 Broadwall, London, SE1 9PL

1 3 5 7 9 10 8 6 4 2

Designed by Design 23

Illustrations by Gary Davidson

ISBN 1 85283 890 6

A catalogue record for this book is available from
the British Library.

An Introduction
by Trev and Simon

(Brought to you in association with the fresh new taste of "Pot-Fish", Britain's number one instant fish snack in a pot!)

Trev: Hello there! Simon and myself have been asked, by the nice people at Comic Relief, to write an introduction to this book, so...

Simon: ...Oh that's easy! 'Here, reader, meet The Squashed Tomato Book ... Squashed Tomato Book, meet your reader... I don't think you've met each other before, have you...?'

Trev: What do you think you're doing?

Simon: An introduction! You said that we...

Trev: Simon, it's not that simple, listen...an introduction requires the writer to draw the reader's attention to the content of the book by igniting the flames of interest and starting the fires of knowledge, thus warming the brain and...

Simon: ...I think your brain has just boiled over! Look, I'll do it, all you have to write is this... 'Hello reader, here's a book full of jokes...blimey! That's good!'

Trev: Is that it!?

Simon: Yeah!

Trev: But what about a discussion on the nature of Jokes? The sociological significance of shared humour, the consequential bonding of...

Simon: Oh dear... sorry Trev, look, we've just run out of space, what a shame. Hard luck, never mind!

Trev: ...Hang on! Hang on! Wait a minute, you can't just cut me off like that, I've got some interesting statistics on humour and jokes...

Simon: Oh...very good Trev, very clever! Let's hear one of your 'really really very funny' jokes then.

Trev: Er...um...ok...er...Knock! Knock!

Simon: Who's there?

Trev: Trev!

Simon: Trev who?

Trev: Me! Trev! Your double-act partner! Ha! Ha!

Simon: Great Trev... very good! Knock! Knock!

Trev: Oh...who's there?

Simon: Simon!

Trev: Simon who?

Simon: Me! Simon! I'm returning your joke... Look, I really think you need to read the book yourself, Trev!

Trev: What book?

Simon: *This* book! The one we're supposed to be writing the introduction for...

Trev: The introduction! Oh, yes! Ok. Here goes...

"Jokes and Their Impact on the Subconscious" Jokes, when verbally distributed

	REALLY REALLY VERY FUNNY
	REALLY FUNNY
	VERY FUNNY
	QUITE FUNNY
	NOT FUNNY

SIMONS JOKES   TREVS JOKES

Oh come on! Please look, can I just squeeze a bit on this page... oh! Poo!

Laugh, I almost died – Delirium at the Doctors

Hello, my name iss Professor Franz von Sillyperson und I am a famous psychiatrist. Please excuse my stupidaccent, but all psychiatrists speak ziss vay.

First, I have to varn you zat zere iss a dangerous person on ze loose in ziss book und to bevare at all times zat he iss not sneakink up on you – but enough about me, let's talk about you.

My first diagnosis iss zat you are stark, starink, ravink, bonkers. How do I know ziss? First... you have bought zis book. Second... you are actually readink ziss nonsense. Zat iss proof enough for me zat you are feelink extremely silly. We must try to find a cure for zis. Zey say zat laughter iss ze best medicine. I don't agree. I zink aspirin iss ze best medicine, but I am villink to give laughter a try.

Read ze following jokes twice a day before meals und see me in ze next chapter. Be careful, I have included some deliberately unfunny jokes in a bid to catch you out. Don't let me hear laughing at zem... OR ELSE!

"Doctor, it's about this peanuts and banana diet you've put me on.
It's making me act strangely."
"If you stop scratching and come down from those curtains Mrs Jones,
I'll have a look at you."

"Doctor, doctor, I've just swallowed my flute."
"It could have been worse... at least you don't play the grand piano."

"Doctor, doctor, my nose is running!"
"Well tell me which race it's in and I'll put a fiver on it."

"Why did you run out of the operating theatre just as you were about to have your operation?"
"Because the nurse said to be brave and that there was nothing to worry about
as it was a minor operation."
"So? That should have put you at ease..."
"Yes, but she was talking to the surgeon!"

**"Doctor, doctor, I snore so loudly that I keep waking myself up in the
middle of the night. What do you suggest?"**
"Sleep in another room."

"Ah, Mr Jenkins, I haven't seen you for a while." "I know, doctor... I've been ill."

"Wally, why are you looking so depressed?"
"I've just been to the doctor and he told me I had to take
one of these pills every day for the rest of my life."
"What's so terrible about that?"
"He only gave me three pills."

"Doctor, doctor, I think I'm a cat."
"How long has this been going on?"
"Ever since I was a kitten! "

"Doctor, doctor, I can't stop telling fibs." "I don't believe you."

"Doctor, doctor, I think I'm a sheep!" "Open your mouth and say 'BAAA.'"

"Doctor, doctor, I've just fallen off an 80 foot ladder."
"Are you hurt?"
"No, I was standing on the bottom rung."

Patient: "Well, doctor, what's the news?"
Doctor: "I'm afraid you could die any minute now. Is there anyone you want to see?"
"Yes... ANOTHER DOCTOR!"

"Doctor, doctor, is there a cure for sleepwalking?"
"Yes, put drawing pins on your bedroom floor."

"Doctor, doctor, I'm so forgetful."
"Well, sit down and tell me all about it."
"About what?"

Two doctors meet in the surgery.
First Doctor: "Hello doctor, and how am I today?"
Second doctor: "You're very well thank you, how am I?"

"Doctor, doctor, I've lost my mind!"
"Well it's no good coming to me, report it to the police."

Doctor: "Mrs Blenkinsop, have you had this illness before?"
Mrs Blenkinsop: "Yes doctor, I have."
Doctor: "Well, I'm afraid you've got it again."

Doctor: "I'm going to take your temperature."
Patient: "Why - haven't you got one of your own?"

Patient: "Doctor, doctor! I keep thinking I'm a dog!"
Doctor: "I see. Lie on the couch, please."
Patient: "I can't! I'm not allowed on the furniture!"

Patient: "Doctor, you've got to help me. People keep ignoring me."
Doctor: "Next!"

Patient: Doctor, doctor! How can I stop my nose from running?"
Doctor: "Hide its trainers."

Fred: "Our doctor's brilliant. He cured my mum of biting her nails."
Bill: "What did he do, give her some medicine?"
Fred: "No, he pulled all her teeth out."

"Doctor, doctor, I think I'm a tie." "Go and get knotted."

Jimmy: "Why are you drinking your beer with a blindfold on?"
Wally: "Because my doctor told me I must never look at another drink."

"Doctor, I've got a problem... I have to go to the toilet at six o'clock every morning."
"What's the problem with that?"
"I don't get up until seven!"

"Doctor, doctor, I'm an incurable thief." "I've got something you can take."

"Doctor, doctor, I'm having trouble with my diet."
"What have you been eating?"
"Snooker balls... I have three reds for breakfast - a brown,
a yellow and blue for lunch - and the black and the pink for supper."
"Aha...the problem is, you're not eating enough greens."

"Doctor, doctor, I think I'm a lavatory." "Don't be potty."

"Doctor, doctor, I think I'm a mine shaft." "We'll soon get to the bottom of this."

"Doctor, doctor, I think I'm a billiard ball." "Go to the end of the cue."

Doctor: "Have your eyes ever been checked?"
Patient: "No, they've always been brown."

"Doctor, doctor... I've got terrible wind.
Is there anything you can give me for it?
"Yes, a kite."

"Doctor, doctor, I hope I'm ill."
"You hope you're ill, whatever do you mean?"
"I'd hate to feel this bad and find out that I'm well."

Doctor: "Stop screaming - I haven't come near you with this injection yet!"
Patient: "I know, but you're standing on my foot."

Squashed Tomatoes On Toast

Hello, I am Pierre Stew and this is my brother Francois.
We are the famous *Stew Brothers*, the world's best SQUASHED TOMATO chefs.

Francois: We will start with Squashed Tomatoes on Toast.

Pierre: You need two tomatoes, two slices of bread, butter, salt, pepper.

Francois: Cut the tomatoes in half and fry them in butter for five minutes, turning once.
Put the bread in the toaster and when it is done, butter the toast.

Pierre: When the tomatoes are fried, MANGLE, SQUASH and PULVERISE them.
SHOW NO MERCY.
Put the SQUASHED TOMATOES onto the toast.
Add salt and pepper and eat them.

Always ask a grown-up before starting a recipe or using the cooker.

Family Misfortunes and Relative Nonsense

Hello again, readers. Feelink better? No? Vell, do not giff up hope yet. Zere iss still time for ze sillyness cure to work vith zis section on Family Misfortunes. Zere is nothink so amusink as to see some kind of disaster befall a member of your family... for example, pushink your dad in a slimy, tadpole-infested pond is good fun. Of course, your dad vill not agree with zis unless he iss pretty silly, too.

To find out how silly he iss, und to continue your laughter cure, tell him ze following jokes. If he laughs und slips around the room singing, "I'm a little goblin", zen he is just as silly as you are. If, on ze other hand, he tells you to shut up or he vill stop your pocket money until you are 93, zen his iss perfectly normal.

Zis test works on mums, too. I once suspected zat my mum had a silly streak when she started doink strange dances when she got up in ze morning. However, I had to change my diagnosis ven I found out my sister had put itchink powder in her knickers.

An old man was out shopping with his old wife. They had just put all their goods through the check-out, when the supermarket girl asked: *"Carrier bag?"* The old man replied: *"No thanks, she can walk."*

Katy: "Mum, why do you get grey hairs?"
Mum: "Well, Katy, it's because of all the worry and trouble you cause me."
Katy: "Well, you must have been horrid to granny!"

"Charlie, why are you being sick?"
"I've been in the garden doing bird impressions, mum."
"How do bird impressions make you sick?"
"I was eating worms."

Auntie Cordelia was showing her bored nephew photographs of her holiday in Blackpool. However, Terry perked up when he saw one of his aunt sitting on a donkey at the beach. *"Ooh, I like that one of you Auntie... but who is that sitting on your back?"*

Auntie Mavis: "You're a quiet little girl today, Sally... why is that?"
Sally: "Mum's giving me 50p an hour not to mention that wart on your nose!"

Simon came home from his first day at school and his mum asked:
"Well, what did you learn on you first day, then?"
"The first thing I learned was that my real name is Simon and not
  Mummy's Little Darling."

Frank: "Grandad, have you really never been wrong about anything?"
Grandad: "I must confess to one occasion. It was when I thought I was wrong
about something, but then realised I wasn't."

Dad: *"This report is terrible Kenny. Your teacher says that he finds it is impossible
to teach you anything."*
Kenny: *"I told you that teacher was no good."*

Jamie decided that he was fed up with all the rules and regulations at home so he
decided to run away and told his mum that he was off. Ten minutes after leaving, he was
back. *"What's the matter?"* asked his mum. *"You didn't get very far."*
"Only because I'm not allowed to cross the road on my own."

"Robert, go and kiss your auntie good-bye." "Why mum, what have I done wrong?"

Billy on his new bike: "Look mum, no hands."
A few minutes later: "Look mum, no feet."
Still later: "Look mum, no *TEETH!*"

Dad: "Look son, there are some geese on the wing."
Son: "That's strange, I always thought the wings were on the geese."

"Mum... I haven't been able to get to sleep for two nights."
"*Why is that?*"
"Ever since Dad broke his leg and the doctor told him not to go up the stairs,
 he has been making such a racket climbing up the drainpipe."

Mum: "That son of ours... I never know when he is telling fibs."
Dad: "That's easy, it's whenever his lips are moving."

"Grandad, why do you think you have lived to such an old age?"
"Well it's probably because I was born such a long time ago!"

Peter: "*Mum, I don't like kippers and custard on toast.*"
Mum: "*How do you know, you've never tried it before.*"

"Dad, are you still growing?"
"I don't think so, why do you ask?"
"Well, it's because the top of your head is coming through your hair."

Fred: "I've just learned to swim."
Wally: "That's nothing, I learned to swim a long time ago. My dad took me to the middle of a lake in a boat and threw me over the side, so I had to swim back to the shore on my own. The only difficult bit was getting out of the sack."

Brian was always misbehaving and his mum was worried about him going to his friend's birthday party. "Now, I have told Mrs Smith that if you are any trouble, she is to send you home immediately." Brian was only gone 15 minutes, before he was back home again and his mum sent him straight to bed without any supper. A little while later, she went upstairs to ask what he had done wrong to be sent home so early. He replied: "I didn't do anything wrong... the party isn't until next week."

Why did Wally eat wallpaper and drink magnolia paint?
He wanted to be an interior decorator, like his dad.

Auntie Doris: "Stephen, that new haircut looks lovely!"
Stephen: "I'd better have it done again then!"

"Hey Belinda, I eated four bits of toast for breakfast!"
"Don't you mean 'ate'?"
"Okay, I eated EIGHT bits of toast for breakfast."

Dad: "Larry... come here. I'll teach you to break the glass in my greenhouse with your football!"
Larry: "It's alright dad, I already know how."

"Hello, Mrs Smith, I have come to tune your piano for you."
"But I didn't ask for the piano to be tuned!"
"No, but the rest of your family did!"

"Dad, dad... what are our ancestors?"
"Well, son, they are your forefathers."
"I didn't know I had four fathers. Where are the others?"

Peter decided he could no longer put up with his friend's interfering sister, who was ruining their game of football. "I'm fed up with this... why don't you tell your sister to go away." "My sister?" wailed his friend. "I thought she was your sister."

"Dad, there's a man outside collecting for the local Old Folks' Home... shall I give him grandad?"

Susan and her dad were out walking in the countryside.
"Oh look, Daddy," said Susan, "there's a whole flock of cows."
"Not flock," answered her father, "herd".
"Heard of what?"
"Herd of cows."
"'Course I have."
"No. A COW HERD."
" It probably did. You're shouting!"

"Dad, dad... I've got a great scheme for saving money!"
"That's good news, what is it?"
"Buy me a bike, and I won't wear out my shoes so quickly."

"Dad, which hand do you usually use to brush your teeth with?"
"My right hand of course."
"That's odd, 'cos I use my toothbrush."

Mum was ill and William was trying to be helpful by making her a cup of tea. However, after hunting for 15 minutes, he still could not find the tea bags, so he went to ask his mum where they were.

"William, you really are silly... they're in the top cupboard, behind the pickles, in a biscuit box clearly marked 'Sugar' of course!"

"Harry, don't you know it's rude to whisper in front of Auntie May?"
"Sorry mum, I was just saying what a big nose Auntie May has and I thought it would have been rude to say it out loud."

Dad at the pet shop: *"I would like a puppy for my son please."*
Assistant: *"I'm sorry sir, we don't do swops."*

Mum: "Bobby, why are you crying?"
Bobby: "Because the baby bit me, mum."
Mum: "Bobby, he's too young to know that it hurts."
Mum *again:* "Bobby, why is the baby crying?"
Bobby: "It's okay mum, he knows that it hurts now!"

The World Famous Stew Brothers

Tomato and Mozzarella Salad

Pierre: This is a very simple and tasty dish, eaten often as a starter by the italians. For this recipe, we have to be reasonably kind to the tomatoes and avoid SQUASHING, GRINDING and MUTILATING them.

Francois: All you will need is a large beef tomato, a piece of mozzarella cheese about the same size as the tomato, olive oil, fresh basil, salt and pepper.

Pierre: Simply cut the tomato and the mozzarella into thin slices and arrange on a plate so that each piece of tomato is next to a piece of cheese.

Francois: Finely chop the fresh basil and sprinkle over the tomato and cheese. Gently pour the olive oil all over the dish, so that everything is covered by a very thin film of oil.

Pierre: Add salt and pepper to taste and eat cool.

Always ask a grown-up before starting a recipe or using the cooker.

Classroom Cackles and School Daze

Vell, vell, vell. How iss ze treatment goink? Ziss next section should make you happier as it deals vith ze only people who are madder than you... teachers!

Ze reason teachers are mad iss that they are ze only people in ze vorld who vant to go back to school when they are grown up... a sure sign of being ZIPPEDY-WOBBLE-DING-DEDOODAH if you ask me.

What makes teachers even madder iss that they go to a special place called Teacher Training School... where they learn how to go back to school. Pretty stupid in my opinion.

When I was at school, I was alvays at ze top of my class. Ze teacher used to make me sit on ze roof, which was about as amusing as certain gags in zis section, I can tell you.

Teacher: "Where did King John sign the Magna Carta?"
Jimmy: "At the bottom of the page."

Teacher: "Tessa, what's five plus five?"
Tessa: "Er, eleven miss."
Teacher: "That's wrong... five plus five equals ten."
Tessa: "But miss, last week, you said four plus six equals *ten!*"

Teacher: "Now, I've got a little job for someone to do, but it needs a child who is responsible."
Chris: "I'll do it miss, I'm responsible."
Teacher: "What makes you think that, Chris?"
Chris: "Well miss, when the classroom window was broken, I was responsible, and when you found a toad in your desk, I was responsible for that, too."

Teacher: *"You're working hard there, Barney, what are you making?"*
Barney: *"A portable."*
Teacher: *"A portable what?"*
Barney: *"I don't know yet, sir, I've only made the handle."*

Teacher: "Colin, you look very pale this morning, have you been ill?"
Colin: "No miss, my mum made me wash my face today."

Teacher: "If coffee is £1.20 a pound, Sidney, how much coffee could you buy if you had 30p?
Sidney: "None sir."
Teacher: "None... that's ridiculous. Why?"
Sidney: "If I had 30p, I could buy a bar of chocolate."

Teacher: "What did your dad say about your school report, Henry?"
Henry: "Do you want me to include the swear words sir?"
Teacher: "No, leave out the swear words - what else did he say?"
Henry: "Nothing."

Teacher: "Billy, why aren't you doing your drawing?"
Billy: "'Cos I ain't got no pencils, miss."
Teacher: "BILLY... that's terrible - you know it's 'I haven't got any pencils, you haven't got any pencils, they haven't got any pencils."
Billy: "Who has got all the pencils then?"

Teacher: "Gary, give me a sentence starting with the letter 'I.'"
Gary: "I is..."
Teacher: "No, Gary... AM always comes after I, not IS."
Gary: "Okay sir. I AM the letter that comes before J.

Teacher: "Terry, when I was your age, I could name all the kings and queens of England."
Terry: "But there had only been a couple of them when you were my age sir."

Headmaster: "I'm very disappointed in you, Davis, you used to be joint top of the class and now you are bottom of the class... what is your explanation?"

Davis: "It's teacher's fault sir."

Headmaster: "How can it be teacher's fault?"

Davis: "She stopped me from copying my homework from the boy who is still at the top of the class."

Teacher: "Darrell, what is your favourite food?"
Darrell: "Spaghetti bolognese, miss."
Teacher: "Spell it."
Darrell: "Actually, I think I prefer beef."

Teacher: "Greg Jones, is this football yours?"
Greg: "Er... did it break anything sir?"
Teacher: "No, not that I know of."
Greg: "Then, yes sir, it is mine."

Clive said to his mum: "I wish I lived in the olden days."
"Why?" asked his mum. "
'Cos there wouldn't have been so much history to learn."

"Mum, I'm not allowed to do home economics any more, because I burned something in cookery class." "That's a bit harsh, what did you burn?" *"The school."*

Alan was boasting to his teacher one day. "My sister and I know all the words in the English dictionary between us sir," he said. "Oh yes," said the teacher. "And what does the word 'stipendiary' mean then?" "That's one of the words my sister knows."

Teacher: "What's the definition of 'illegal'?" Pupil: "A sick bird of prey."

Teacher: "Alex, did you know that Richard II once banned cricket during his reign?"
Alex: "Yes sir, his reign stopped play."

Teacher: "Tommy, if you had four bars of chocolate and Arnold took two, what would you have?"
Tommy: "A fight."

Teacher: "Wally - give me a sentence that contains the word 'fascinate.'"
Wally: "Er... my jacket has got nine buttons, but I can only fascin-ate."

Teacher: *"Sally, are you having trouble with that question?"*
Sally: *"No sir, it's the answer that's causing the trouble."*

Dad: "Son... this is terrible you have come 25th in a class of 25. It couldn't be worse."
Son: "Yes it could, dad, I could have been in a class of 30."

Teacher: "Alex and Ian, your results have been terrible. You will both stay behind and write out your full names a hundred times... Alex, why are you crying?"

Alex: "It's not fair, miss, his full name is Ian Smith and mine is Alexander Cholmondely-Blenkinsop!"

Teacher: "Tommy, what letter comes after A?"   *Tommy:* "All of them, sir."

Teacher: **"Rachel... I hope I didn't just catch you copying from Jeremy's paper!"**
Rachel: **"I hope you didn't catch me, too!"**

Three children were in the playground, discussing what their biggest faults were.
The first boy said: *"I just can't help it, I keep on copying my homework from other people, but I never get caught."*
The second lad said: *"My trouble is that I just can't seem to stop firing ink pellets at the teacher and he never sees me do it."*
The two boys then asked the girl who was with them what her biggest fault was.
"Oh, my biggest fault is that I'm always telling on people to teacher," she replied.

Dad: "How did you do in your history exam?"
Son: "I only got one question wrong."
Dad: "That's very good, so you got all the rest right then?"
Son: "Er no, I didn't do the others."

Teacher: "Now, James, if mother had five children, but only four potatoes, what would be the best way for her to share the potatoes out equally?
James: "Make mash."

Teacher: "Why did Henry VIII have so many wives?"   Nick: "Because he liked to chop and change."

Teacher: "Stan. I wish you would pay a little attention."
Stan: "I'm paying as little as I can."

"Help, help, I can't swim," screamed a boy
in the school swimming pool.
"So what," replied his friend at the poolside.
"I can't do my homework,
but I don't tell everyone about it."

Teacher: "Tell me Darren, what do
you like best about school?"
Darren: "When it's closed."

Voice on the phone: "I'm sorry, headmaster, but Simon Davis is ill and won't be able to come to school today."
Headmaster: "Oh, I'm sorry to hear that. May I ask who is speaking?"
Voice: "Yes, this is my father speaking."

The World Famous *Stew Brothers*

Spaghetti in SQUASHED TOMATO sauce

Francois: This one is a bit more difficult.
It is spaghetti in SQUASHED TOMATO SAUCE.

Pierre: You will need a small onion, a tin of
SQUASHED TOMATOES, a large spoonful
of tomato paste, some basil and oregano,
garlic powder, salt, pepper, oil and a
teaspoon full of sugar.

Francois: Using a saucepan, fry the chopped onion gently in oil until it goes clear.
Add two pinches each of garlic powder, oregano, and basil.

Pierre: Stir for a while, then add the tin of SQUASHED TOMATOES (chopped tomatoes
will probably do), a little water, the spoon of tomato puree, the sugar and the salt and
pepper. MASH the mixture together and simmer for 15 minutes.

Francois: "Meanwhile, cook the spaghetti in boiling
water for eight to ten minutes. Drain the spaghetti,
rinse in boiling water and serve with the sauce and
parmesan cheese."

**Always ask a grown-up before starting
a recipe or using the cooker.**

Animal Crackers and Zany Zoology

Still readink zis book are you?
Then you are obviously still
BOING-ZIP-BEBOP-QUACK-QUACK,
as we say in ze profession.

If you had been cured, zis book vould be
at ze bottom of your cat litter tray by now.

"HALIBUT-MERCEDES-
CORNFLAKES-PLATYPUS."
Who said zat? Me? Oh, I am sorry.
I haff not been feelink well lately.
Perhaps it is all these terrible jokes.

Anyvay, onto ze next section, which iss about animals. I am very fond of animals,
especially with a little tomato ketchup and chips.

My dog is often tellink me zat animals are more intelligent than man, but I don't
always understand what he iss sayink, because he only speaks Japanese, French and
Spanish. How stupid of him not to speak English. He is barking mad.

It is believed dolphins are ze cleverest animals of them all. Ha! If so, why do they live
in ze sea, where it is cold and salty and there is no TV?

What did the beaver say to the tree? "Nice to gnaw you."

Paul: "Would you like to play with our new dog?"
Peter: "Oh, I don't know, he looks a bit big. Does he bite?"
Paul: "That's what I want to find out."

What do Australians do with a wombat? Play wom.

The ferocious lion decided that he wasn't getting enough respect around the jungle. So he stalked off and roared at a giraffe, saying: *"Who is the Lord of the Jungle?"* The frightened giraffe replied: *"You are, of course."* The lion did this to several animals before he came up to the elephant. He roared loudly at the elephant and asked: *"Who is the Lord of the jungle?"* The elephant picked up the lion with his trunk and swung him around his head until the lion said: *"Stop it - there's no need to get in a huff just 'cos you don't know the answer."*

What do you get if you cross an elephant with a fish? Swimming trunks.

Why do humming birds hum? Because they don't know the words.

What did the earwig shout as he jumped over the cliff? *"Ear-wi-go!"*

What happened when the dog biscuit factory went bust? They sent in the official retriever.

What is the difference between African elephants and Indian elephants?
About 3,000 miles.

Who do you call if your underwater grand piano sounds wrong? *The piano TUNA.*

The young tern asked its mum: "Can I have a baby sister please?"
The mother tern thought for a while and replied: "Yes, you've been well
behaved... and one good tern deserves another!"

What is a hedgehog's favourite food? Prickled onions.

Why does a giraffe have such a long neck?
Because its head is so far from its body.

What do you call a fly with no wings? *A walk!*

Two men on safari were taking photographs, when they noticed an angry cheetah,
the fastest animal on earth, about to charge them. One of the photographers quickly
started changing into his training shoes. His companion said: *"Don't be ridiculous,
you'll never be able to run faster than a cheetah."* The first photographer said:
*"Who cares about running faster than the cheetah... as long as I can run faster than
you, it doesn't matter."*

What's the definition of a tiger? A lion in its pyjamas.

If a quadru-ped has four legs and a bi-ped has two legs. What is a tiger? *Stri-ped.*

What is big, white, fierce and furry and has a hole in the middle? A Polo bear.

How do you know if there is an elephant under your bed? Your nose touches the ceiling.

"That's a nice dog... what is his name?"
"I don't know, he won't tell me."

A young lad was working at a farm during the school holidays and the farmer told him to count the sheep in a field. Quick as a flash, the youngster replied: *"There are 517 sheep in the field."* The farmer was amazed. *"How did you count them so quickly?"* he asked. *"Easy,"* said the boy. *"I just counted their legs and divided the total by four."*

Where do injured wasps go? To the waspital.

Wally went into the pub one day and noticed a huge Rottweiler dog lying behind the bar. Wally asked the landlord: *"Does your dog bite?"* The landlord replied: *"No, he doesn't."* So Wally bent down to pat the Rottweiler, which took a massive snap at him and bit his hand off. *"I thought you said your dog didn't bite,"* he wailed. The landlord replied: *"That is not my dog."*

Bob and Christian were both prawns and Bob was a bit fed up with being one of the smallest creatures in the sea. So one day he went off to see the magic white whale. "I'm fed up with being bullied by the bigger creatures in the sea... what can I do?" he asked the whale. "With my magic powers, I could turn you into an enormous shark," said the whale. Bob thought this was great and immediately agreed. However, after being a shark for a while, he got fed up because everyone was scared of him and he had no friends.
So he went back to the whale and got himself turned back into a prawn. He went in search of his old friend, Christian, but got a frosty welcome.
Christian said: "No, I don't know any prawns called Bob.
I used to know one, but he's a shark now." "No, no, look," said Bob. "It's really me... I'm a Prawn-Again Christian!"

What goes "Tick-tock-woof?" A watch dog.

What is black and white and red all over? A penguin with sunburn.

How do animals keep up with current affairs? *They watch the six o' clock gnus.*

What do you do to save a mouse that's stopped breathing?
Give it mouse-to-mouse resuscitation.

What is a cat's favourite breakfast cereal? Mice crispies.

What do sheep wear when they go to school? *Ewe-niforms.*

Why did the hedgehog push his friend under the steam roller? He wanted a flat mate.

Which animal performs operations underwater.
An orthopaedic sturgeon.

"I've lost my dog."
"Why don't you put an advertisement in the newspaper?"
"Don't be stupid, my dog can't read."

What bird has got wings but cannot fly? Roast duck.

Baked Tomatoes with Onion and Soured Cream

Francois: This is another easy tomato dish, which unfortunately involves being quite kind to the tomatoes.

Pierre: All you need is couple of large tomatoes, some grated cheese, a small amount of finely chopped onion, two large spoonfuls of soured cream and some oregano, as well as salt and pepper.

Francois: Cut the tomatoes in half and put in a dish. Sprinkle them with a small amount of finely chopped onion. Put the tomatoes and onions in a hot oven for about ten minutes.

Pierre: While they are in the oven, grate the cheese and mix it with the two spoons of soured cream and the oregano.

Francois: Take the baked tomatoes out of the oven and cover with the cheesy cream sauce. Sprinkle some more grated cheese on top.

Pierre: Return the tomatoes to the oven and cook for another ten minutes.
Add salt and pepper to taste and serve piping hot.

**Always ask a grown-up before starting
a recipe or using the cooker.**

Monster Madness and Ghostly Giggles

"DACHSHUND-TABLECLOTH-BUBBLE-TOMATOES."
Er, sorry, readers. I didn't know you vere listenink.I keep hearink these strange voices tellink me that I am mad. Impossible, of course.

We haff now arrived at ze supernatural chapter. Things zat go "BUMP" in ze night are very scary and not at all funny... unless it is your sister fallink out of bed.

When I was young, my cruel parents used regularly to send me to visit a horrible, slimy, warty, creature, who used to drool everyvere and slobber all over me. It was only when I grew up that I learned that ze creature was my aunt.

Anyvay, it iss my opinion zat ze only people who are scared of mosters and believe in them are frothing, salivating, drooling, loonies. So there!

"GRRRRRRRRRROOOOOOOOOOOWWWWWWWWWWWLLLLLLLLLLLLLLLLL!!!!!!"

Ach, mein Gott... a monster. Help, help. Run awaaaaaaaaaaaay!

What do gourmet monsters eat for starters? Garlic Fred.

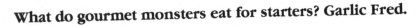

Voice on the phone: "Hello is that the police?"
Policeman: "Yes, what can we do to help?"
Voice: "There's a burglar been caught up at the haunted house.
Can you come up and get him?"
Policeman: "Who is this calling?"
Voice: "The burglar!"

What do French monsters eat? Frogmen's legs.

First ghost: "How did you meet your wife?"
Second ghost: "Our eyes met across a crowded dance floor and it was love at first fright."

Esmeralda: "How did you know that horse was going to win the Grand National?"
Quasimodo: "Oh, it was just a hunch."

Who do ghosts employ to do their washing up? The vile green hairy-lipped squid.

How do you kill a vampire painter?
Put a stake through his art.

What did the mummy ghost say to her noisy children?
"Spook only when you're spooken to."

What do monsters buy when they want to eat tinned seafood? Submarines.

What type of bicycles do poverty-stricken skeletons drive? Boneshakers.

Why does Frankenstein get indigestion? Because he always bolts his food.

What do mummy swamp things give their children when they are ill? Rod's liver oil."

John: "How can you scare away vampires?
Pete: "With garlic."
John: "How do you get them to eat the garlic?"

Dad monster: "I've got an upset tummy.
Mummy monster: "It must be someone you ate."

What's green, ten feet tall and tastes disgusting? The inedible hulk.

What's the crack regiment in the Ghoulies' army called? *The Special Scare Service*. What is its motto? *Who Scares Wins*.

What do ghosts use to clean up spilled paint? Methylated spirit.

What's a monster's favourite food? Jake and Sidney pie.

Billy: "Dad, dad... there are monsters in my wardrobe!"
Dad: "No there aren't."
Billy: "Why don't you check?"
Dad: "Alright, just to humour you. Are there any monsters in there?"
Growly voice from the wardrobe: "No. No monsters in here."
Dad: "See, I told you there were no monsters in there."

Mr Monster: "Doctor, doctor, I don't feel well."
Dr Swamp-Creature: "What have you been eating?"
Mr Monster: "Last night, I ate boiled Smiths. For breakfast I had fried Bloggs and for lunch I ate some baked Harrisons."
Dr Swamp-Creature: "You're not eating enough Greens."

What is a monster's favourite take away meal? Ronald MacDonald.

What do monsters call people in cars? Meals on wheels.

What type of cars to wealthy ghouls drive? Rolls Royce Silver Ghosts.

What do monsters like to drink? Slimeade.

What's a ghost's favourite food? Ghoul-ash.

What do witches put on their newts-tail salad? Salad scream.

What do ghosts and monsters use to play cricket with? Vampire bats.

What is Count Dracula's favourite cocktail? A tequila sundown.

What do trolls like in there fruit salad? Granny Smith.

Young monster: "Mum, I don't like people."
Mummy monster: "I know, dear, but if you smother them in ketchup,
you won't notice the taste."

What do you call a fairy who hasn't had a wash for a week? Stinkerbell.

SQUASHED TOMATO
and Cheese Omelette

Pierre: This one is my favourite –
SQUASHED TOMATO and
cheese omelette.

Francois: You will need one small,
ripe tomato, two eggs, some milk, oil,
salt, pepper and a little grated cheese.

Pierre: CHOP the tomato into little pieces and fry for a few minutes in a little oil.
Take out the fried tomato and CRUSH it until it begs for mercy.

Francois: BEAT the eggs with salt, pepper and a splash of milk until the mixture is
limp with fright and put into the pan with a little oil. Fry gently until the omelette is
firm on the bottom and creamy on top.

Pierre: Sprinkle the SQUASHED TOMATO and grated cheese over the
omelette. Fold the omelette and cook for one minute till the bottom is
light brown.

Francois: Turn it over and cook the other side till it too is light
brown. Eat hot.

Always ask a grown-up before starting a recipe or using the cooker.

The Trouser-Munchingly Funny Joke Section

What? Still readink zis rubbish? Some of zose last jokes vere so bad und so old, zey vere not even funny in pre-historic times.

Zings around here are becomink extremely silly. Ze next batch of jokes have just been delivered to me by a green-haired circus clown riding in ze pouch of a pink kangaroo. He said zey vere ze funniest jokes he had ever heard. I said zat I did not zink so. He told me I would not be able to stop myself from laughing at his jokes. I told him zat I would eat my trousers if zese jokes had me laughing.

Anyvon have some ketchup?

"Dad, dad, there's a man at the door with a bill."
"Really? What did he say?
"Quack, quack."

Wally was very interested when a man started gathering up horse manure from the road outside his house.
Wally: *"Why are you collecting all that horse manure?"*
Man: *"To put it on my rhubarb."*
Wally: *"You should come to my house, I get custard on mine."*

Mrs Barnes: "When God was handing out noses, I thought he said roses and I asked for a large, red one."
Mrs Simpkins: "That's nothing... when God was handing out chins, I thought he said gins, so I asked for a double."

What's brown and smelly and runs through Egypt? The Sewage Canal.

A brave knight was injured in battle and lost his horse. After many days of crawling in agony, he arrived at a huge castle, where he knocked on the door and demanded to see the owner. The Lord of the Castle arrived and asked what he could do to help. The knight said: *"I am a brave knight and I have lost my horse in battle. Can you lend me another, so I can rejoin my army?"* The Lord said: *"Well, we've run out of horses, but I could lend you this Dachshund."* *"Don't be so cruel,"* cried the Knight. *"You can't turn a knight out on a dog like this."*

Why did the Mexican push his wife out of a window? Tequila.

What do you call an ancient king, who spends his time cutting cheese into very small slivers?
Alfred the Grater.

"Knock, knock."
"Who's there?"
"Stan."
"Stan who?"
"Stan-d aside... I'm coming in anyway."

"Knock, knock."
"Who's there?"
"Harry."
"Harry who?"
"Harry up and let me in, it's freezing out here."

"Knock, knock."
"Who's there?"
"Iris."
"Iris who?"
"Iris-t you on suspicion of murder."

"Knock, knock."
"Who's there?"
"Don."
"Don who?"
"Don'cha ever open this door?"

"Knock, knock."
"Who's there?"
"Tim."
"Tim who?"
"Tiiiiim-berrrrrr! There's a tree falling on your house."

"Knock, knock."
"Who's there?"
"Soldier."
"Soldier who?"
"Soldier a door bell last week. Doesn't it work?"

"Knock, knock."
"Who's there?"
"Toby."
"Toby who?"
"Toby... or not Toby? That is the question."

"Knock, knock."
"Who's there?"
"Ivory."
"Ivory who?"
"Ivory much hope you will open the door."

Mrs Wally: "Wally's in hospital. He had an accident while ironing the curtains."
Wally's friend: "Did he burn himself?"
Mrs Wally: "No, he fell out of the window."

What do you call two raincoats in a cemetery? Max Bygraves.

What do you do if you see a blue banana? Try to cheer it up.

Barber: "How would you like you hair cut, sir?"
Customer: "Off!"

It was a cold winter's day and Wally said to his wife: "I've got a lovely, roaring fire going in the lounge."
Mrs Wally replied: "But we don't have a fire place."

What do you call an ant that likes helping people? An assist-ant.

"Mum, mum, what's that in the garden?"
"That's a poodle."
"Really? I thought it was a dog."

Why did the bald man paint rabbits on his head?
Because, from a distance, they look like hares.

How do you stop your dog digging up the garden? Hide the spade.

Why did Wally give up his tap dancing lessons? He kept falling in the sink.

A grumpy Martian landed his spaceship on the pavement outside a piano shop, went inside and walked up to one of the pianos. "Take me to your leader, quick!" he snarled at the piano. "And wipe that stupid grin off your face!"

What is the similarity between a baboon and a man being followed by a koala? *They have both got a bear behind.*

Wally: "I've just discovered a great invention, which helps me to look through concrete walls."
Wally's friend: "Really... what is it?"
Wally: "A window."

What is tall and wobbly, and stands in the middle of Paris? The Trifle Tower.

What do you get if you drop a ten ton weight into a goldfish pond? Flat fish.

What happened to the aging prawn who went for a night out at the underwater disco? *He pulled a mussel.*

Tuna Fish and Tomato Salad

Pierre: This is a delicious salad which makes a very filling meal. It is ideal for the summertime and picnics especially, although there is minimal violence to the tomatoes.

Francois: You will need four tomatoes, one hard-boiled egg, half a small onion, a small tin of tuna fish, some fresh basil, salt, pepper and some French dressing.

Pierre: First you must hard boil the egg. To do this, put the egg in boiling water. Bring back to the boil and cook for about ten minutes. Place it immediately under cold water and allow to cool down completely.

Francois: Peel the egg and cut into thin slices. Also cut the onion into very fine rings and slice the tomatoes. Place the slices of tomatoes and onion on a plate. Next, open the tin of tuna fish and flake all over the salad.

Pierre: Decorate the salad with the slices of egg and garnish with the finely chopped fresh basil. Add salt and pepper and French dressing to taste. Voila. This is especially nice with crusty French bread.

Always ask a grown-up before starting a recipe or using the cooker.

Military Mayhem and Laughs with the Law

Right readers. Stand to attention and listen carefully. That Professor von Sillyperson chappie was obviously stark, staring bonkers and a very dangerous person to have in charge of a book, if you ask me.

My name is Major Disaster and I've taken over the running of the Squashed Tomato book, so the rest of this operation is going to run smoothly.

Quite frankly, some of the jokes have been so bad, they were bound to send people crazy like that poor von Sillyperson person.
From now on, we are going to have good jokes, told with military precision.
Remember, bad jokes can get you killed... by the person you're telling them to.

What did the policeman say to his stomach?
"Right, you... I've got you under a vest!"

The Duke of Wellington was at the Battle of Waterloo, when one of his soldiers came up to him and complained that his shoes were leaking and he was getting wet feet. One of the Duke's lieutenants said to the soldier: *"Why don't you wear a pair of Wellingtons?"* But the Duke said: *"He doesn't take my size."*

What did the judge do to the elastic band thief?
Sent him to jail for a long stretch.

Colonel: "Soldier, what would happen if both your ears were shot off in battle?"
Soldier: "I wouldn't be able to see."
Colonel: "Surely you mean hear?"
Soldier: "No sir, if my ears were shot off, my helmet would fall over my eyes."

Police chief: "Inspector, have you caught the burglar who stole the lavatory from the police station?"
Inspector: "No sir. We've nothing to go on."

Why did Wally the bank robber sleep on the floor?
Because he thought it was best to lie low for a while.

What do you call a French general who has just exploded?
Napoleon Blownapart.

Which regiment only recruits babies? The Infant-ry.

Which month do soldiers dread most? March.

Bank manager: "Help, police... we've been raided by a hole-in-the-wall gang."
Policeman: "Don't worry sir, we'll look into it."

At which battle did King Harold die? His last one.

Judge: "Prisoner. Are you guilty or not guilty?"
Prisoner: "I don't know. I haven't heard the evidence yet."

Policeman: *"Why did you shoot that man six times?"*
Wally: *"I ran out of bullets."*

Wally: "I think I should be a detective?"
Wally's friend: "Why?"
Wally: "Because I'm always helping the police with their inquiries."

**What do you call a secret agent carrying a yellow rabbit?
The Man with the Golden Bun.**

Wally and his two friends, Bob and Peter, had just escaped from jail, but the police had almost caught up with them. As a last resort, they hid in three sacks they found. When the police arrived at the scene, one of them prodded the sack in which Bob was hiding. Bob went: "*Miaow, miaow.*" So the policeman said to his colleagues: "*It's only a cat.*" The same happened when Peter's sack was prodded. He said: "*Woof, woof.*" So the officer told the other police: "*There's only a dog inside.*" At last, he went up to the third sack, where Wally was hiding, and prodded it. Wally thought his friends had been clever, so he adopted the same ruse, saying: "*Apples, lovely fresh apples.*"

Judge: "Have you ever been up before the court before?"
Criminal: "I don't know. What time does the court usually get up?"

What do you call a soldier who is laughing, but won't tell you why? Private Joke.

Policeman: "Wally... this is the 51st time I've caught you stealing apples. What have you got to say for yourself?"
"Wally: "Well, if it wasn't for me, you would be out of a job."

General: "Right, men, this is a very dangerous mission which requires a brave man with acute hearing."
Cowardly soldier: "I'd volunteer sir, but I don't wear cute earrings."

Detective: *"Wally, we have no evidence to prove that you committed this robbery. You're free to go."*
Wally: "Great. Does that mean I can keep the money?"

How did soldiers have their armour sent to them in the olden days? By chain mail.

The Duke of Wellington had just won the Battle of Waterloo and went over to speak to his captured adversary, the great Napoleon. Napoleon said: *"Congratulations on your win, how did you do it?"*
The Duke: *"I prayed to God before the battle."*
Napoleon: *"But I prayed to God before the battle and I didn't win."*
The Duke: *"That's because God doesn't understand French."*

Bald man: "I say inspector, my wig has been stolen. Has it been handed in?"
Policeman: "Not yet sir, but we are combing the area.

Judge: "Wally Pratt, I sentence you to 999 years in jail."
Wally: "That's a relief. I thought I was going to get life."

What did the policeman say to the man he caught doing a raid at MacDonalds?
"I arrest you for being a hamburglar."

Convict to new prisoner: *"How long did you get?"*
New prisoner: *"Life."*
Convict: *"I'd better move to the bunk by the door. I'll be leaving before you."*

Wally at the police station: "I've come for the job advertised outside."
Policeman: "What job advertised outside?"
Wally: "The one on the sign that says 'Man Wanted for Burglary.'"

What do you give a soldier who has been naughty? Corporal punishment.

Wally's dad: "You know, Wally... one of our ancestors was killed at Waterloo."
Wally: "Which platform?"

Two soldiers went out for a night on the town, but missed the last bus back to their barracks. Scared that they were going to get into trouble, they decided to go to the depot to steal one. One of the soldiers went inside to get the bus, while the other stood guard outside. After an hour, there was still no sign of a bus, so the soldier outside went into the depot, where he saw his friend looking puzzled amongst a row of double-deckers. *"What's the matter... why haven't you got us a bus?"* he asked. *"Well, the bus that takes us to the barracks is a number nine, and there isn't one here,"* he replied. *"That's alright,"* said the first soldier, *"We'll steal a number eleven and change at Broad Street."*

Sergeant-major: "Right, you 'orrible lot. When I say leap, I want you to jump as high as a building." When he gave his command, all the new recruits jumped as high as they could... except one. Apoplectic with rage, the sergeant-major demanded: "Why didn't you jump, you 'orrible little man?" *Recruit:* "I was only obeying orders. You said jump as high as a building and buildings can't jump."

Why are guardsmen always so cold? Because they are always in bearskins.

Bacon, lettuce and SQUASHED TOMATO Sandwich

Francois: For a tasty snack, why not try the bacon lettuce and SQUASHED TOMATO sandwich.

Pierre: All you need is two slices of bread, two rashers of bacon, some lettuce, mayonnaise, butter, salt, pepper and a ripe tomato.

Francois: Lightly fry the bacon in some butter. Meanwhile, MANGLE, CRUSH and PULVERISE the ripe tomato until it whimpers for forgiveness.

Pierre: Have a quick rest, then butter the two slices of bread. Put the SQUASHED TOMATO on one slice. Add salt and pepper. On the other slice, slap on a layer of mayonnaise and a few small pieces of lettuce.

Francois: Take the sizzling bacon from the pan and sandwich between the two slices. Simple, but very tasty.

Always ask a grown-up before starting a recipe or using the cooker.

Travel Trouble and Mechanical Mayhem

Okay, readers. Stand at ease. It's becoming quite clear that you're all as daft as that Professor von Sillyperson chap.

He probably served in the Scottish Army, where all the soldiers wear skirts. I know that I would never wear a skirt as part of my uniform.
I only wear a skirt when I'm off duty.

Anyway, that's quite enough about skirts.
They have nothing to do with this chapter,
which is about cars and other things like that.

Personally, I'm against all this transport
nonsense. A good walk never hurt anyone.
In the Army, we always march everywhere.
Going by car turns people into softies.
Anyway, my skirt always gets caught
in car doors.

What do you call a rusty car that's afraid of the dark? A nervous wreck.

What do you call a man who used to like farm vehicles? An ex-tractor fan.

Wally was building a rocket, which he planned to fly to the sun. A famous astronaut laughed at him, saying: *"As soon as you get near the sun, your rocket will be burned to a cinder."* Wally replied: *"No, it won't. I'm going at night."*

Traffic policeman: "Do you realise you have been doing 100 miles an hour?" Wally: "That's impossible. I've only been driving for five minutes."

What's the best way to get a seat on a bus? Get a job as a bus driver.

Wally drove his car out of a petrol station, not bothering to look where he was going. In doing so, he made a massive lorry swerve to avoid him and it smashed straight into the petrol pumps, causing a huge explosion. Wally heaved a sigh of relief, saying: *"That was lucky. I got out of that petrol station just in time."*

Wally was up in a three-engined aeroplane, when the captain made an announcement. "I'm afraid our number one engine has broken down. This will mean the flight will be 30 minutes late." *A few minutes later, the captain came on again and said:* "Engine number two has broken down now. But don't worry, it only means we will now be one hour late." *Wally turned to the next passenger and said:* "I hope the other engine doesn't pack up, or we'll be up here all night."

A policeman was amazed to see an old lady driving her car at 90 miles per hour, while doing her knitting at the same time. The officer eventually caught up with her and yelled: *"Pull over."* She replied: *"No. It's a pair of socks."*

Wally and his two friends, Bob and Peter, had broken down in the desert, and they each decided to carry one thing with them on the long walk back home. Bob decided to take the water and Peter grabbed the sandwiches. Wally wanted to take a car door with him, so Bob and Peter asked why. Wally replied: *"Well, if it gets too hot, I can always wind down the window ."*

Traffic policeman: "You idiot. Don't you realise this is a one way street."
Wally: "But I was only driving one way."

Two birds watched amazed as Concorde flew past at supersonic speed. One bird said: "It's incredible. How does it go so fast? The other replied: "I bet you would go that fast if your tail was on fire."

Wally's friend: "How did you get that puncture?"
Wally: "It must have been that fork in the road."

Customer: *"I want to buy a new car.*
Salesman: *"What make of car would you like?"*
Customer: *"Lada."*
Salesman: *"I SAID 'WHAT MAKE OF CAR WOULD YOU LIKE?'"*

Passenger: "Driver. Does this bus run on time?"
Driver: "No. It runs on diesel."

What do you call an underground train full of full of clever people?
A tube of smarties.

Boss: "Wally. I want you to take this can of paint, then go to the front of the house and paint my porch." Half an hour later, Wally came back and reported: "I've finished the job sir. But, by the way, it wasn't a Porsche... it was a Ferrari."

Customer: "I'd like a windscreen wiper for my Skoda."
Mechanic: "Sounds like a fair swap to me."

How do you double the price of a Skoda? Fill it with petrol.

Why do Skodas have heated rear windows?
So the drivers don't get cold hands when they push them home.

What do you call an open-topped Skoda? A wheelbarrow.

What's the difference between a Skoda and your sister's clothes?
It's less embarrassing to be seen in your sister's clothes.

What do you call it when a Skoda does 50 miles an hour on the motorway? *A miracle.*

Why are kangaroos such bad drivers? They are always jumping the lights.

What do you call a man with a car on his head? Jack.

Robert: "What type of car has your dad got?"
Alan: "I don't know the name, but it starts with a 'J'."
Robert: "That's odd, our car starts with a key."

What do you say when your car goes to the breaker's yard? Rust in peace.

Why do pigs make such bad drivers?
Because they are road hogs.

An old lady bought herself a Volkswagen Beetle, not realising that the engine was in the back. After a few months the car broke down while she was out with a friend. *"Oh dear,"* said her friend. *"You're engine's conked out."* *"That's alright,"* said the old lady. *"I've got a spare one in the boot."*

What happened when Wally tried to blow up a car?
He burned his mouth on the exhaust pipe.

What do cars do before they play football? They change into football gear

Wally was so pleased with his new training shoes, he decided to challenge Nigel Mansell's racing car to a trial of speed. Unbelievably, on the last lap, Wally was way out in front and was about to go first past the chequered flag when he suddenly smashed into the crash barriers. Mansell went on to win, but he went back to congratulate the injured Wally on a great effort. *"What happened on the last bend? If you hadn't crashed you would have won,"* asked Mansell.
Wally replied: *"I had a blow-out in one of my trainers."*

**Why was Wally fired from his job on a submarine?
He kept sleeping with windows open.**

What did the traffic lights say to the car? "Don't look, I'm changing."

How do you get two whales in a Mini?
Straight up the M4.
How do you get four whales in a Mini?
Two in the back, two in the front.

Stuffed Tomatoes

Pierre: This is a delicious and filling dish, which does not require much preparation. Cruelty to the tomatoes is minimal.

Francois: You will need two large tomatoes, a slice of ham, a small amount of grated cheese, four very large mushrooms, a quarter of a small onion and a quarter of a small green pepper, some oil, a little basil and a spoonful of natural yoghurt.

Always ask a grown-up before starting a recipe or using the cooker.

Pierre: Slice the tops off the tomatoes, and scoop out the pips inside. Throw away the pips. Finely chop the onion, mushrooms and pepper and fry lightly for a few minutes with the basil until tender.

Francois: Cut the ham into small pieces and grate the cheese. Mix the ham and cheese with the cooked onion, mushroom and green pepper. Add the yoghurt and mix well.

Pierre: Fill the two tomatoes with the mixture and sprinkle with grated cheese. Sprinkle on some basil.

Francois: You don't have to dress up as a tomato to make this dish, but it is traditional down on our French funny farm.

There's a Joke in My Soup – and Other Food Funnies

Wakey, wakey! This next section is about about waiters and the awful food they serve.

My mother's cooking was so bad, I joined the French Foreign Legion to try to forget about it. Unfortunately, my mum wrote to the General and told him to make sure that I ate all my greens.

They say that Army food is very tasty. My dad certainly agrees. He left the Army forty years ago... and he can still taste it.

About these "Waiter Waiter" jokes. They're traditionally very bad, so it's best to have a military strategy before you tell them to anyone. I suggest that you sneak up behind your "victim", shout the joke out very quickly and run away very fast before he has time to hit you.

"Waiter, waiter, this soup tastes funny."
"Then why aren't you laughing, sir?"

"Waiter, waiter, fetch me the chef."
"I'm afraid he's gone to another restaurant for lunch, sir."

"Waiter, waiter, do you have toad in the hole?"
"No sir, just a frog in my throat."

"Waiter, waiter, these onions are tough."
"But, sir, they're spring onions."
"I must have eaten one of the springs."

"Waiter, waiter, what do you recommend?"
"Another restaurant, sir."

"Waiter, waiter, this must be the worst soup of the day I've ever had."
"That's because it's yesterday's soup of the day, sir."

"Waiter, waiter, there's a fly in my soup."
"No, sir, that's the manager... the last customer was a magician."

"Waiter, waiter do you keep the kitchens clean?"
"Of course, sir."
"That explains why the food tastes of soap."

"Waiter, waiter, this bowl is full of holes."
"Well, you did ask for LEEK soup, sir."

"Waiter, waiter, I want the fish."
"With pleasure."
"No, you idiot, with chips."

"Waiter, waiter there's a coat on my salad."
"That's just the dressing sir."

A man went into a restaurant and ordered Dover Sole, followed by Aylesbury Duck.
When the fish arrived, he said: *"That sole is not from Dover, bring me another."*
He was satisfied with the second fish but complained when the duck arrived.
"That isn't Aylesbury Duck, bring me another." Eventually he was happy with what was
brought him and wanted to see the chef to compliment him on the tasty meal. He said:
*"Chef... that sole and duck was delicious, so you can't be an English chef. Where do you
come from?"* The chef replied: *"You seem to be the expert sir... you tell me!"*

"Waiter, waiter, I want coffee without cream."
"I'm afraid we've run out of cream sir... would you mind coffee without milk?"

Customer: "Waiter, would you cut my pizza into slices please?"
Waiter: "Yes, sir, would you like me to cut it into four slices or six."
Customer: "Four... I couldn't possibly eat six."

"Waiter, waiter, I'll have the steak and kiddley pie."
"Don't you mean steak and kidney pie, sir?"
"That's what I said, diddle I?"

"Waiter, waiter, the service is terrible."
"Yes sir, but not as bad as the food."

"Waiter, waiter, fetch me the manager, there's a spider in my soup."
"There's no point in getting the manager, he's scared of them, too."

"Waiter, waiter, there's no pork in this pork pie!"
"So what, there's no cat in cat food, is there?"

Waiter: "And what is sir going to have to finish the meal?"
Customer: "Indigestion, probably."

"Waiter, waiter, do you have a white Macon?"
"No, sir, just my normal clothes."

Wally went into a restaurant, where he saw a sign saying *"All you can eat for one pound."*
When the waiter came over, Wally pointed to the sign and said: *"I'll have two pounds worth of that please."*

"Waiter, waiter, these eggs are rotten."
"Don't blame me sir, I only lay the tables."

"Waiter, waiter, fetch me some gravy."
"Of course sir, one lump or two?"

A tramp knocked on the door of a house and asked the woman inside if he could have some food. *"But didn't I give some of my beef stew last week,"* she said indignantly.
"Yes," said the tramp, *"but I'm better now."*

"Waiter, waiter, there's a roof on my plate!"
"Well, sir, you did ask for cottage pie."

"Waiter, waiter, I'm on a seafood diet."
"But, sir, we don't serve seafood."
"That's alright, I just see food... and eat it."

Mum: "Oh no... our dog has eaten the pie I cooked for supper."
Dad: "That's alright, we'll get a new dog tomorrow."

"Waiter, waiter, I can't eat this food."
"Why not sir?"
"You didn't give me a knife and fork."

"Waiter, waiter, this soup tastes foul."
"That's because it's chicken soup."

"Waiter, waiter, I'll have the shepherd's pie."
"But what will the shepherd eat sir?"

"Waiter, waiter, this pie tastes disgusting."
"I'll have you know, sir, the chef has been making pies since before you were born."
"This was obviously one of them."

"Waiter, waiter, I would like some battered fish."
"'That's a bit cruel sir, it's bad enough putting them in the frying pan."

The World Famous *Stew Brothers*
SQUASHED TOMATO pizza buns

Francois: Everyone likes pizza, but if you don't have time to make a real one, our SQUASHED TOMATO pizza buns are excellent substitutes.

Pierre: You will need a bread bap, a ripe tomato, a spoonful of tomato paste and some grated cheese.

Francois: Slice the bap down the middle and toast each side lightly under the grill.

Pierre: Take the tomato, SKIN it and then MUTILATE, GRIND and SQUASH it until limp. When you are no longer limp, mix the SQUASHED TOMATO with the tomato paste.

Francois: Spread the mixture onto the two bits of bap and then sprinkle liberally with grated cheese. Place the two pizza buns under the grill until the cheese is gooey. Eat while hot.

Always ask a grown-up before starting a recipe or using the cooker.

Game for a Laugh and Sporting Slip – Ups

The discipline in this book is absolutely outrageous, what with people sniggering when they shouldn't and then refusing to guffaw loudly at the best gags I've selected. One of the best ways of learning discipline is to play sport, which is what this section is about.

I was very keen on sports at school and I particularly enjoyed athletics. The sports master used to paint a target around my belly button and enter me in the "catching the javelin" event. Very character building. For some reason, I remember spending a lot of my schooldays in hospital. Can't think why.

What do you call a woman snooker player, who can do a maximum break while balancing a pint of lager on her head? *Beatrix Potter.*

Wally: "I went fishing the other day and caught one of those huge fish... what was it called?"
Wally's friend: "A whale?" **Wally:** "Don't be daft. I was using the whale as bait."

WALLY: "I played football with Gazza last week."
WALLY'S FRIEND: "I don't believe you."
WALLY: "I did. This man said to me 'If you're any good at football, then my name's Paul Gascoine.'"

Manager: "Why didn't you stop the ball?"
Goalie: "What are you moaning about? The net stopped it."

Ref to player lying on the pitch: *"You're not really injured, you're just acting. I'm going to book you..."*
Player: *"Aw, ref!"*
Ref: *"...to do the cabaret act at the after-match dinner."*

A doctor had just finished a check-up on a 112-year-old man. Doctor: "Well, Mr Old, you're in very good shape for your age. How do you do it?"
Mr Old: "It's all the exercise I do."
Doctor: "What exercise is that?"
Mr Old: "Every Saturday, I walk ten miles to watch my dad play rugby."

"I'm sorry I missed that penalty, boss. I could kick myself."
"Don't bother... you'll probably miss."

DARREN: "My grandad supports Liverpool and he says they never lost a game in the 1950s."
KEVIN: "Wow. They must have had a great team."
DARREN: "No. My grandad's got a lousy memory."

Why did Wally give up water ski-ing? *He couldn't find a downhill lake.*

"Ref, ref, can't you do something? This bloke keeps punching me."
"Don't be ridiculous, this is a boxing match."

Wally: "I've had a great idea to improve the team."
Manager: "Oh really? When are you leaving?"

Trevor: "I know the scores of every football match before they start."
Barry: "Oh, yeah. How?"
Trevor: "It's always nil-nil before they start."

FOOTBALL MANAGER: "Well done, you were brilliant. I think you had an excellent game to day."
PLAYER: "Thanks, boss, I didn't think I played THAT well."
MANAGER: "...for the other team!"

BRIAN: "My doctor says I should give up rugby?"
SIMON: "Why? Does he think you'll get injured?"
BRIAN: "No - he's seen me play."

Tubby Mathews: *"I've had to give up golf because of my stomach."*
Roger: *"Why? Does it hurt?"*
Tubby: *"No. It's because I can't see over it to hit the ball."*

WORRIED MOUNTAINEER: "Do people often fall off Mount Everest?"
GUIDE: "No, only once."

Football fan: "Shoot Gazza, shoot Gazza!"
Wally: "Why? What has he done?"

Sportsmaster: "That was an excellent 100 metres race Wally. What did you do it in?"
"My sports kit sir."

What is a football fan's favourite ice cream flavour? *Aston Vanilla.*

*The sports trainer decided Wally wasn't fit enough, so he ordered him to run
ten miles every day. A week later, Wally telephoned to say he couldn't be at
the athletics tournament, because he was 70 miles away.*

Wally was furious when the star player in his favourite football team missed a crucial
penalty in the last minute of the match. After watching the action replay, he said: *"I don't
know why they let him take it again. He missed it the first time."*

Fred: "If I had been in goal, we wouldn't have lost five-nil."
Bobby: "You're right. We would have lost ten-nil."

**After losing nine races at the greyhound races, Wally came up with a foolproof plan to win
back his money. He decided to put his money on the hare.**

Why are Manchester United the coolest team in the Premier League?
They've got more fans than any of the others.

**"Doctor, doctor, have you got anything for my athletes foot?"
"How about a pair of training shoes?"**

Why couldn't the cricketer stand up?
Because he was always in the slips.

Wally: *"I want to return this tennis racquet"*
Sports shop assistant: *"Why? What's wrong with it?"*
Wally: *"Since I've had it, I've haven't won a single game."*

Bobby wanted to go to watch Useless Rovers play, so he phoned the ground and asked what time the match started. Not used to having any supporters, the club secretary replied: *"What time can you make it?"*

Wally: "Doctor, will I be able to play football when this plaster is off my leg?"
Doctor: "Of course."
Wally: "Good, because I couldn't play it before."

Why are football pitches always water-logged?
Because the players are always dribbling on them.

MANAGER: "Our new striker has certainly got a footballer's brain."
COACH: "Yes, but it's a shame he hasn't got a footballer's feet."

What is Wally's best position at cricket? Silly mid-off.

A cricket fan's wife was having a baby, but he couldn't tear himself away from the Test Match on TV. However, he kept on phoning the hospital for news of his wife. However, he ended up phoning the cricket scoreline number by mistake, and fainted when he heard the message: *"It's 160 all out... and the last one was a duck."*

Why did the world's best pole-vaulter have to give up the sport?
He was scared of heights.

The World Famous *Stew Brothers*

Naughty Double-doorstep Sandwich

Always ask a grown-up before starting a recipe or using the cooker.

Pierre: This is a delicious doorstep sandwich ideal to fill the biggest gap in the biggest tummy. The tomatoes do not endure too much suffering.

Francois: You will need three thick slices of fresh bread, some cheddar cheese, a slice of ham, one small tomato, butter, salt and pepper, some lettuce, some French mustard and mayonnaise.

Pierre: Take all the slices of bread and butter them. One of the slices, which will go in the middle of the sandwich, will need to be buttered on both sides. Take the first slice of bread and spread with mayonnaise. Put on a layer of lettuce leaves and then add thin slices of cheddar cheese.

Francois: Next, take the slice of bread that has been buttered on both sides and put it on top of the cheese. Spread a little French mustard onto the top and then add the slice of ham. Now, cut the tomato into thin rings and put it on top of the ham. Finally add salt and pepper to taste and cover with the final piece of bread. Then see if you are able to take a bite out of the naughty double doorstep without having to use a car jack to crank your mouth open wide enough!

Jokes So Bad We Had To Invent a New Category for Them

Right you 'orrible little lot. We are nearly at the end of the book and you've managed to avoid being killed by people who can't stand you telling these jokes. Well done!

By brilliant military planning, we've arrived at the last section, in which we've gathered all the worst jokes together for an all-out assault on the enemy.

It's quite clear that telling somebody one of the following jokes would be an outrageous Act of War.

There is only one thing for it. The time for stealth and surprise is over and we must go for open confrontation. But we must be prepared.

Before you tell any of these jokes, I suggest you go to an Army Surplus store and buy a surplus army.

What do you call a man with ear plugs in? Anything you like... he can't hear you.

"Hello, Mrs Brown, can Joe come out to play?" "I'm afraid not, he's got measles."
"Oh... can his bike come out to play instead?"

What do you call an aardvark that's scared of mice? *A vark.*

A man bumped into some penguins walking in the street one day and they all started following him. The confused man eventually went to the police station and said:
"What should I do with these penguins?" "I suggest you take them to the zoo," said the helpful bobby.
The next day the policeman stopped the same man, who was driving a van.
In the back of the van were all the penguins, wearing sunglasses. *"I thought I told you to take them to the zoo,"* said the policeman.
"I did," said the man. *"They liked it so much that today I thought I'd take them to the beach."*

WHAT DO ITALIANS EAT TO CELEBRATE WEDDINGS? CONFETTI BOLOGNESE.

How do you say *"Robert's got a rabid Rottweiler terrier"* without pronouncing the Rs?
Bob's got a mad dog.

What do elves call Do It Yourself? Gnome improvements.

Teacher: "Robin, spell 'Rain'."
Robin: "Er... w-r-a-y-n-e."
Teacher: "Jamie, you try."
Jamie: "Um... r-h-a-g-n-e"
Teacher: "What a terrible spell of rain this is."

Wally: "It's lucky I'm not Chinese!"
Wally's friend: "Why?"
Wally: "Because I can't speak the language."

"Would you like to dance with me?"
"I'm sorry, but my mum told me never to accept an invitation from a perfect stranger!"
"Hey... who said I was perfect?"

MAN AT THE AUCTION: "I've spent a long time bidding for this chimpanzee and he is costing me a lot of money. He had better be clever.
AUCTIONEER: "Of course he is clever, sir. He has been bidding against you."

The phone rings at Wally's house at five o'clock in the morning. Bleary-eyed Wally answers the phone and says: *"Hello."*
Voice on the line: *"Is that the emergency plumber?"*
Wally: *"No, you've got the wrong number."*
Voice: *"Sorry to trouble you at this time in the morning."*
Wally: *"No trouble, I had to get up to answer the phone anyway."*

"Mum, mum, Gavin hit me."
"Did you hit him back?"
"No, I hit him first."

Which vegetables always win the athletics events? The runner beans.

Jimmy's dad gave him 50p pocket money too much by mistake one week, but Jimmy decided to keep quiet about it in case dad didn't notice. However, the following week, Jimmy's dad realised what had happened and gave his son 50p less. *"Hey dad, my pocket money's 50p short this week,"* said Jimmy. *"Yes, but you didn't complain when I gave you 50p too much last week." "Well, everyone's allowed one mistake."*

What do you call a man who steals your money? *Rob.*

Wally's friend: "Your dog must be clever to be able to play chess."
Wally: "Not really. He's only beaten me twice."

Wally and his friend each bought a dog at the pet shop, but couldn't decide how to tell them apart. Wally said: *"I'll tell you what, my dog can have a red collar and your dog can have a blue one."*
Unfortunately, both the collars fell off, but Wally's friend came up with a solution. *"Why don't you keep the black dog and I'll have the white one."*

What do you call a man with a head full of rabbits? Warren.

How do you make a Swiss roll? Push him down a hill.

Wally wanted his name up in lights at every cinema in Britain.
So he changed his name to *"Toilets."*

TV PRESENTER: "I'm sorry, viewers, we were going to have the world's oldest man on the show tonight. I am afraid he has not been able to come, because he is in hospital... visiting his father!"

What do you get if you cross a flock of birds with a tea service? *Flying saucers.*

What did the roof say to the house? I've got you covered.

WALLY: "I would really like to know the exact spot where I am going to die."
WALLY'S FRIEND: "Why?"
WALLY: "Because I would never go there."

What do you call a Russian emperor who likes fruit? Peter the Grape.

What do you call a boomerang that doesn't fly back? A stick.

Where does Kylie buy her kebabs? From Jason's Donner-van.

"What's the difference between an elephant and a Matter-booboo?"
"What's a matter-booboo?"
"Nothing's the matter, Yogi."

Dr Carrot: "Well Mrs Potato, the tests we did have shown that the reason you've been feeling a bit off colour is that you're expecting a happy event."
Mrs Potato: "You mean...?"
Dr Carrot: "Yes, you're going to have chips!"

What was the first animal off the Ark? The one nearest the door!

What do you call a deer with no eyes? No idea.

Okay then, what do you call a deer with no eyes and no legs? Still no idea.

The World Famous **Stew Brothers**

Ham and SQUASHED TOMATO Bake

Francois: For a very tasty meal, you should try our ham and SQUASHED TOMATO bake.

Pierre: All you need are two slices of ham, two tomatoes, some grated cheese, salt and pepper.

Francois: Take the two tomatoes and carefully SKIN them. When they least expect it, MINCE, MANGLE and generally SQUASH them until they stop putting up a fight.

Pierre: Lay out the two slices of ham and spread one of the SQUASHED TOMATOES along the edge of each slice. Add a little salt and pepper.

Francois: Sprinkle grated cheese along the tomato and then roll the ham until the tomato is wrapped up.

Pierre: Sprinkle some more cheese on top of the ham. Put the ham slices in a dish and bake for 10 minutes. Eat hot.

Always ask a grown-up before starting a recipe or using the cooker.

THE SERIOUS BIT – A Message From Comic Relief

It all began in 1985 and now, eight years on, Comic Relief has raised over £70 million, every penny of which has gone to support projects in Africa and the UK. The face behind the big red nose is an organisation called Charity Projects, a charity committed to raising money in a fun way and making everyone aware of the serious side of giving grants. The money raised is allocated in a responsible and effective way, making sure that all fundraising costs are covered by generous sponsorship from the business world.

This means that every penny *you* raise goes straight to help fund aid projects and none is soaked up by administration costs at Comic Relief.

Looking back over the past eight years from the first No. 1 hit single when Cliff Richard and the Young Ones got themselves a "crying, talking, sleeping, walking, living doll" to the one where Mr Bean didn't get elected (despite the help of Bruce Dickinson from Iron Maiden), The Red Nose has captured the imagination of the public. The very first night of comedy at the Shaftesbury Theatre, along with the "Living Doll" single, raised over one million pounds. It was clear then that a phenomenon was in the making.

The roll call that night was amazing – Lenny Henry, Rowan Atkinson, French and Saunders, Smith and Jones, Fry and Laurie, Rik Mayall, Billy Connolly and many more. Since that night, they have remained committed to the cause and continued to help. No one, it seems, is unhappy to become involved when the call comes.

The germ of the idea that was Comic Relief went into hyperdrive with the *probiscus rubus* – the Red Nose. No one can quite remember who actually had the idea, although there is the theory that it involved Ade Edmonson, a rake, a fridge door and a house brick. Quite how all those elements came together, no one is really sure, but one thing which is absolutely certain is that the idea culminated in six TV hours of the very best of British Comedy combined with serious films from Africa and the UK. This gave a focus for the public's desire to do something which might make a difference. It also gave them the chance to go crazy, have fun, humiliate their friends and raise millions upon millions of pounds.

The first Red Nose Day saw an outbreak of city gents wearing the lovely little red things and gently saying hello to their fellow commuters. By Red Nose Day 2, no Mini or Rolls Royce was safe – the Car Nose was born. As Hale and Pace "stonked" their way through Red Nose Day 3, the noses had even attacked buildings. The invasion will continue on Red Nose Day 4 when a new breed of nose will appear in places you couldn't imagine.

The public have done some amazing things in the name of Comic Relief. They have jumped out of aeroplanes, sat in porridge, maggots or raw eggs, bathed in onion gravy, eaten dinner underwater, abseiled down town halls, auctioned off teachers and sixth formers, composed songs, gunked anything that moved and there have even been nude skiers wearing nothing but carefully attached red noses! No scout, guide or brownie has failed in their duty. No headmaster or teacher has suffered in vain. Millions of red noses have inspired hundreds of thousands of sponsored events.

The result is that Red Nose money in Africa has built wells, sown seeds, perfomed operations, immunised children, clothed refugees and transported food and blankets. Here in the UK it has housed homeless people, provided emergency beds, sheltered vulnerable women, taught young people about the dangers of drugs and alcohol, made buildings and transport available to the disabled and stood up for their rights as well as those of the nation's pensioners.

So much work has been done and mothers, fathers, sons, daughters, uncles, aunts, friends and neighbours throughout the UK have made it all possible. There is still more work to do and while that situation remains, the Comic Relief team will work as hard as ever to get it done.